mac's year

1992

Cartoons from the *Daily Mail*

Stan McMurtry **mac**

Edited by Mark Bryant

Chapmans

For Nick and Mary Spargo

Chapmans Publishers Ltd
141–143 Drury Lane
London WC2B 5TB

First published by Chapmans 1992

Selection and Text by Mark Bryant

ISBN 1–85592–730–6

Printed and bound in Great Britain by
Clays Ltd, St Ives plc

A Management Today investigation revealed that up to 90% of union expenditure went on lavish headquarters and the salaries and expenses of officials and staff.

'Bad news I'm afraid. A comrade who complained about the way union funds are spent has bled all over the Axminster . . .' *2 August*

A 7554-tonne liner chartered for a South African millionaire's daughter's wedding party sank in the Indian Ocean after an explosion. The Greek crew were accused of deserting the ship whilst 580 passengers remained on board.

'So, after shouting "Women and children first", then what did you do, captain?' *6 August*

Scotland Yard reported that up to half of of all beggars on London's streets are confidence tricksters organized in rings who treat begging as a business.

'Don't be ridiculous! I'm in the same business – this is my night off.' *8 August*

After 1943 days, TV news journalist John McCarthy was freed from captivity in Damascus. His personal message from Islamic Jihad to the UN Secretary General raised hopes that other Western hostages would be freed soon.

Fifty-five Million Yellow Ribbons *9 August*

In an effort to increase their popularity with female voters, Labour announced a plan to open men's clubs to women. However, there was concern lest disaffected male members should switch their support in consequence.

'Not very bright those feminist gels, were they, turning up to protest about men-only clubs on the Glorious Twelfth? *13 August*

Israel's leader, Yitzshak Shamir, agreed to trade up to 400 Arab prisoners for British, US and Israeli captives in Lebanon, the first signs that diplomatic pressure might prevail in the Middle East hostage crisis.

'Is that a glimmer of light I see? *15 August*

As specialist firefighter Red Adair fought to cap the burning wells that were a legacy of the Gulf War, it was reported that Iraq was to be allowed to trade its oil on world markets once more.

'I hear Saddam Hussein is being allowed to sell his oil again . . .' *16 August*

In a reactionary backlash by the military, Soviet leader Gorbachev was arrested and tanks besieged the Russian Parliament building in Moscow. The coup failed, signalling the final collapse of Communism in the USSR. *22 August*

In the aftermath of the coup it was Boris Yeltsin, the 61-year-old President of the Russian Federation, who was seen as the hero of the hour, with Mikhail Gorbachev increasingly marginalized.

'Sorry I'm late. I had to clean up all crime, catch a falling airliner and avert World War III on the way here . . . *23 August*

As statues were pulled down in the Soviet Republics, Britain's own symbols of Communism began to totter. *Morning Star* sales slumped to 10,000 copies a week and there were fears for Marx's bronze bust in Highgate Cemetery.

'I don't care if anyone does desecrate it! Take it back to Highgate Cemetery now!' *27 August*

Prime Minister John Major, visiting President Bush for a two-day Anglo-American summit to coordinate a huge international relief programme for the former Soviet Union, declared that the West wouldn't let Russia starve.

'He just did it again, George, honey – he slipped six vol-au-vents and a salmon mousse down his trouser leg . . .' *29 August*

Popular long-serving *News at Ten* anchorman, Sir Alastair Burnet, took early retirement and turned down a £250,000 golden handshake when cuts were announced at ITN.

'We were going to make do with a little blue plaque but the taxidermist's estimate was so reasonable . . .' *30 August*

At the Labour Party conference in Brighton, Neil Kinnock promised to purge the party of Militant but denied that he had betrayed his left-wing beliefs to win votes.

'Okay, Roy, that's Militant dealt with – what's next on the agenda?' *30 September*

German golfer Bernhard Langer failed to sink a six-foot putt in the last hole of the Ryder Cup, held on Kiawah Island in South Carolina's alligator country, giving the US team victory over the Europeans.

'See? I told you once the cameras had gone, the Europeans might throw us something . . .' *1 October*

Spurs soccer star Paul Gascoigne required a knee operation at the Princess Grace Hospital in London following an incident in a nightclub. Gazza later withdrew claims that he had been attacked by a mystery man.

'There, Gazza. Nurse Blenkinsop has chased those three pink elephants, the purple rhinoceros and the man who hurt your knee from the room.' *3 October*

Speaking in Brighton, Roy Hattersley signalled that a Labour Government would relax immigration laws to allow in more asylum-seekers and refugees.

'No, no, later – we're not in yet!' *4 October*

Only days before the Conservative Party Conference opened in Blackpool, the Director of Public Prosecutions, Sir Allan Green, resigned after being caught kerb-crawling.

'Slow down to about fifty and we'll jump, Parker – don't want any police accusations of kerb crawling.' *7 October*

As speculation mounted as to who would win the Booker Prize for fiction, NHS chief executive Duncan Nichol attacked Labour's claims that the Health Service was to be privatized.

'. . . and now, ladies and gentlemen, the first prize for fiction . . .' *8 October*

Transport Secretary Malcolm Rifkind announced a new route for the proposed Chunnel rail link, to the dismay of BR who had bought up 1000 homes along the previous route and stood to lose £32 million.

'Before we have another Labour smear – it's pure coincidence that the new route goes through the homes of Kinnock, Hattersley, Robin Cook and John Smith . . .' *10 October*

Heavyweight Sumo wrestlers at the Royal Albert Hall staged the first official tournament held outside Japan as Health Secretary William Waldegrave attacked Labour's claims about the future of the NHS.

'How would you like to go, Mr Kinnock – NHS or private?' *11 October*

US Supreme Court candidate Clarence Thomas faced a Senate Judicial Committee inquiry after allegations of sexual harassment were made by a former student. After a 103-day televised hearing he was acquitted.

'Do you remember sexually harassing me by offering to share your chocolate biscuits in 1976? *14 October*

Military leaders felt betrayed when plans to slim down the Army were announced by Defence Secretary Tom King so soon after the Iraq conflict. Anti-cuts campaigners presented petitions containing a million signatures.

'I have a petition here supporting my defence cuts – signed by Saddam Hussein and thousands of Iraqis . . .' *15 October*

In the biggest shake-up in the history of commercial television, a franchise auction ousted the network's largest company, Thames, as well as TV-am, the breakfast channel run by Bruce Gyngell.

'Nice to see you're staying in the business, Mr Gyngell.' *18 October*

Having beaten France, England's hopes in the Rugby World Cup soared as they prepared to face Scotland in the semi-final. Meanwhile, the Judge Thomas sexual harassment case remained in the public eye.

'Ah, Mr Bumstrode. I was just demonstrating to your secretary a few tactics our gallant rugby lads might employ against the Scots next Saturday.' *21 October*

Lucy Marshall, 24, daughter of a Buckingham Palace clerk living in the Royal Mews, was arrested following a police investigation into a drugs ring.

'Well, they don't normally behave like this after a Bob Martin's conditioning powder . . .' *22 October*

Seymour Hersh's book, *The Samson Option*, sparked off the 'Mirrorgate' scandal in which the paper's foreign editor was claimed to be an Israeli spy whilst supremo Robert Maxwell himself allegedly had Mossad connections.

'**Gerald! Someone from Mossad says we haven't paid the paper bill . . .**' *24 October*

British wives were given the legal right to say 'No' when the House of Lords overturned a 250-year ruling that there was no such thing as rape within marriage.

'Trust you to be awkward!' *25 October*

England came from behind to beat Scotland 9–6 in the Rugby World Cup semi-final.

'That reminds me – who won at Murrayfield?' *28 October*

Arab faced Jew in a historic Middle East summit convened by peace-brokers Bush and Gorbachev in Madrid's Royal Palace.

Middle East Get-Together *31 October*

President Bush put pressure on Israeli PM Shamir to accept a land-for-peace initiative regarding the Israeli-occupied territories of Gaza, the Golan Heights and the West Bank.

'I think we're getting somewhere, Yitzhak. They say they worship the ground you walk on . . .' *1 November*

Beleaguered commuters received a boost when Chancellor Lamont announced increased funding for public transport, including £2 billion for BR in 1993. Railway employees also welcomed the news . . .

'British Rail apologishes for the delay . . . Hic! . . . but driver Gribshaw ish paralytic and hash locked himself in the shtoreroom with Miss Binks of accounts . . .' *8 November*

After 35 years of experiment, a research team in Oxford succeeded in creating energy by nuclear fusion, the same reaction that takes place in the heart of the sun.

'Why couldn't you have been a nuclear scientist? Doreen's husband has harnessed the power of the sun.' *12 November*

A 27-year-old Pakistani seeking political asylum was imprisoned and recommended for deportation after masterminding a massive 'phone home' fraud for immigrants which cost British Telecom £170,000.

'Mummy says she's not going to be outdone by any bogus refugee . . .' *14 November*

Five million bottles of Lucozade were destroyed when police foiled a
contamination plot by animal rights activists claiming that the drink's
manufacturers, SmithKline Beecham, used animals for research in its drugs
division.

'We've just had word – it's safe to go back on to Lucozade again.' *15 November*

In the run-up to the crucial Maastricht EC summit, Mrs Thatcher put party loyalty above personal doubts and backed John Major's stance on Europe . . . for the time being.

'Oh no, Maggie – not another full moon!' *18 November*

After 1763 days, the Archbishop of Canterbury's former envoy Terry Waite was freed in Damascus and told the world of his five-year nightmare manacled to a wall. US hostage Tom Sutherland was released with him.

'At last – what we've all wanted for Christmas . . .' *19 November*

An inquiry was held following allegations on a Thames TV programme that two IRA suspects who had escaped from Brixton prison in July had been aided by Special Branch officers hoping to be led to terrorist bases.

'I sentence you to 20 years' imprisonment and one year's intensive course by the Special Branch on how to escape . . .' *22 November*

Mrs Thatcher caused embarrassment in Maastricht when she broke her silence and called for a referendum on the issue of a single currency. Meanwhile, US oil-fire specialist Red Adair put out the last of Iraq's flaming wells.

'It was one hell of a struggle, Mr Major, but we managed it – positively the last uncontrolled gusher in Kuwait capped . . .' *25 November*

'Isn't that wonderful, darling – Malcolm's been made head girl.' *26 November*

In the biggest ever revolt against the Shops Act preventing Sunday trading, recession-hit supermarket giants Tesco, Asda and Safeway opened thousands of stores despite protests from 'Keep Sunday Special' campaigners.

'Much as I appreciate the gesture, Miss Spilsbury, I fear that holding the managers of Tesco, Asda and Safeway hostage in the crypt will solve nothing . . .' *28 November*

After the release on appeal of the Birmingham Six, Guildford Four and Maguire Seven, a Royal Commission on Criminal Justice was set up under Lord Runciman.

'Of course it feels like solitary, Mauler – you're the only one who hasn't appealed.' *29 November*

In a concerted effort to boost flagging sales, Sunday trading began in earnest with Sainsbury's, Ratners, Boots and BHS joining in to flout the Shops Act and promising to open every Sunday until Christmas.

'You'd be grumpy if you had to work all day on Sunday too, you spotty-faced little git!' *2 December*

After nearly seven years and more than 1000 shows, Terry Wogan decided to quit the BBC when his £500,000-a-year contract expired in February.

'I'm sorry, Terry, but the suit, the wig and the teeth are all property of the BBC.' *3 December*

The Church of England's House of Bishops ruled that homosexual partnerships amongst the clergy were permissible provided they remained celibate.

'. . . and do you, Eric of the gorgeous eyes and cute dimples, take Susan to be your lawful wife – or would you like to change your mind?' *5 December*

Following the suicide of press tycoon Robert Maxwell, Serious Fraud Office investigators were called in to track down £330 million missing from the pension funds of the Mirror Group and Maxwell Communications Corporation.

'All right, go ahead, issue a writ! – Just answer the questions!' *6 December*

As European Commission president Jacques Delors attacked the British stance against a federal European superstate in Maastricht, there were fears by some that PM John Major's resolve would weaken.

'For the last time! – I don't want room service and I don't want any advice!' *9 December*

The Pearson Group and a management-buyout consortium were front-runners in the bid to take over the Mirror Group, but speculation mounted with rumours that Australian Kerry Packer and Lonrho's Tiny Rowland were interested.

'Tiny Rowland won't be long. He's just slipped out to buy a paper . . .' *10 December*

John Major's performance at Maastricht was praised by most Tories but was received with less enthusiasm elsewhere, some critics drawing parallels with Neville Chamberlain's return from Munich.

Peace in Our Time *12 December*

In the wake of the Maxwell affair it was revealed that many high-street banks faced huge losses through unsecured loans to the *Mirror* chief. The biggest single creditor, Lloyds, was owed £197 million.

'We don't have any cash at the moment but if you'd care to wait, our manager is just tunnelling under Barclays . . .' *13 December*

In declaring that they supported the European Social Charter, Labour were attacked by Conservatives who claimed that they would tax 1.75 million part-time and casual workers, many of whom were women.

'Well, did Mr Kinnock confirm or deny he's going to tax part-time, low-paid workers?' *21 January*

Baby Daniel, the year-old son of the late Lord Moynihan's fifth wife, was declared his official heir after a legal tussle involving another claimant whose mother ran a massage parlour in Manila.

'You're welcome of course, Lord Moynihan. But I'm afraid you'll have to ask your mother to find alternative premises.' *24 January*

The 50th-anniversary edition of Radio 4's *Desert Island Discs* featured cricket-loving Prime Minister John Major, who chose a replica of The Oval as his luxury item.

'Gosh. Who'd have thought it, Norma? Me on *Desert Island Discs*... Whatever next? *27 January*

As the Institute for Fiscal Studies questioned whether Labour's taxation plans were sufficient to fund their proposed spending on the NHS, education and transport, further doubts were cast on the party's election prospects.

'I think Kinnock's starting to panic. *30 January*

In an attempt to prevent the former Soviet Union's redundant nuclear scientists from selling themselves to dangerous regimes, PM John Major offered them jobs in Britain at a minium of £35,000 a year.

'You were told the rules, Mr Vladinski – No smoking, no women and no splitting the atom in the bedrooms!' *31 January*

Allegations in the *Sunday Times* that Neil Kinnock had close links with the Kremlin were denied as smears by a former KGB intelligence chief.

'Let them try dismissing this as a smear – kinky sex romps of Roy Hattersley's uncle's next-door neighbour's dog . . .' *3 February*

The Princess of Wales broke tradition to become the first member of the Royal Family to own a foreign car, a metallic-red 157 mph Mercedes-Benz 500 SL.

'This'll put the cat amongst the pigeons – the Queen Mother buying a Harley-Davidson . . .' *6 February*

Documents stolen from Paddy Ashdown's solicitor's office told of the Liberal Democrat leader's five-month affair with his secretary in 1986. Ironically, the revelations appeared to enhance his popularity.

'Neil, d'you remember Blodwen – that smooch behind the cycle-sheds, Cardiff Grammar, 1954 . . .?'
10 February

Company magazine revealed that in a recent survey 37% of men questioned had been sexually harassed by female managers and some had been promised better work prospects if they slept with their female boss.

'Attention, everybody! I'm looking for a new head of department . . .' *11 February*

World heavyweight champion boxer, Mike Tyson, was found guilty of raping Miss Black America contestant, Desirée Washington, by a court in Indianapolis.

'Aw c'mon McClusky. It may be only for ten years. Your new cellmate's gonna need someone to spar with.' *13 February*

The Guinness II fraud trial collapsed when defendant Roger Seelig was deemed mentally unfit to continue. The five-month trial, costing £1.3 million, led to calls for cheaper and quicker legal procedures in such cases.

'**Better not have a retrial just yet – most of us are not mentally fit enough to continue . . .**' *14 February*

Scotland Yard figures showed that 1991 was the worst-ever year for crime, with reported offences soaring to 925,000. Burglaries alone rose by 25,000 cases to 200,000.

'Honestly, I didn't steal it, I won it – it's the Burgular of the Year award.' *17 February*

Neil Kinnock, speaking on London Weekend Television, dismissed John Major
as a far less formidable opponent than Margaret Thatcher.

'Yes, I read it too. – Thank you and goodnight, Maggie!' *18 February*

Cecil Parkinson's former mistress, Sara Keays, was awarded £105,000 in damages from *New Woman Magazine* which claimed she was a 'kiss-and-tell bimbo'.

'Please, luv, help an old woman down on her luck – call me a gold-digging bimbo . . .' *21 February*

In a keynote speech in Glasgow, PM John Major delivered a strong defence of the union of England and Scotland and warned against the dangers of independence or Labour's plans involving a separate parliament.

'It walked in this morning – I think it wants to stay British.' *24 February*

Royal protocol was ruffled on the Queen's State Visit to Australia when Prime Minister Paul Keating placed his arm around Her Majesty to guide her towards dignitaries outside the parliament building.

'What do you think, Philip? I had it made up by the Palace Electrician to stop people putting their arms round me . . .' *27 February*

The United Nations threatened military action against Saddam Hussein if he didn't comply with a demand to scrap Scud-missile factories in Iraq.

'Memo to President Bush. Stop . . . Sneaking suspicion Saddam is not destroying Scud missiles. Stop . . . But has persuaded fellow countrymen to hide them about their persons. Stop . . .' *2 March*

Drivers faced detours of up to 75 miles when part of the M4 was closed so that a crumbling 2045-tonne section of the Ingst road bridge could be transported along it for demolition.

3 March

BR unveiled its much-heralded 'Passengers' Charter' offering compensation to travellers for the late-running of trains. The Consumers' Association claimed it was a 'glossy public-relations con'.

'Driver Wilkinson's bang on time again. An inspiration to us all – he just doesn't stop at stations.' *5 March*

A 41-year-old Cambridge angler was alleged to be a cheat by *Angling Times* when photographs of him holding three prize-winning giant pike over a period of two years were claimed to be of the same fish.

'Well, I think he's cheating – that's the same fisherman he was photographed with twice before'

6 March

A bonanza, giveaway budget was predicted to try and kickstart Britain's flagging economy and stimulate consumer spending. Home Office statistics, meanwhile, confirmed earlier figures about the growing crime-rate.

'Not now, luv – I want to see what's in the Budget.' *10 March*

The Prime Minister ended months of waiting and media speculation by naming the date of the General Election as 9 April. The public, already showing signs of election fatigue, faced the 30-day campaign with mixed feelings.

'We wondered if you had any vacancies until April the 10th?' *12 March*

Labour's claims that an 18-month-old girl died because of inadequate NHS funding were attacked as 'monstrous'. Benetton's recent advertising campaign showing a new-born baby had also caused public disquiet.

13 March

Shadow Chancellor John Smith unveiled Labour's 'alternative budget' which would raise the top rate of tax from 40p to 50p in the pound for those earning over £40,000 per year.

'That's convinced me! If they can afford boiling oil, they can afford higher taxes!' *16 March*

Buckingham Palace announced the official separation of the Duke and Duchess of York as the media continued to speculate about a possible rift between Prince Charles and Diana.

'You realize, if this gets out it'll be the last straw for the Queen. . .' *19 March*

85% of South Africa's 3.3 million white voters backed President de Klerk's referendum opening the way to black-majority rule. The neo-Nazi para military Afrikaner Resistance Movement were opposed to reforms.

'Oh, I'm dreamin' of a Black Christmas . . .' *20 March*

The government claimed that Labour tax plans would hit middle-income, middle-class voters. Meanwhile British Airways examined all seven supersonic Concordes when a large piece of rudder fell off one.

'I bet he's a middle-class pilot on about £36,000 a year . . .' *23 March*

After government pressure, BSkyB satellite TV allowed the BBC to screen 30-minute extracts from the World Cup cricket final between England and Pakistan. 10 million extra viewers could now watch the match.

'Let's see . . . today I'll be canvassing coatless in the freezing cold rain, so tomorrow I'm afraid I'll be confined indoors with a heavy cold . . .' *24 March*

After 151 years *Punch* magazine closed down on 8 April, with losses running at more than £1 million a year and circulation down from 175,000 to 33,000.

'I suppose they're trying their best, but I'm going to miss *Punch*.' *26 March*

Labour's election broadcast featuring a five-year-old NHS patient with an ear complaint who waited 11 months for surgery caused a storm of controversy. The 64th Oscars ceremony took place in Los Angeles.

'. . . And now, for his memorable performance in the fantasy tale of a little girl with earache . . .' *30 March*

An international tug-of-war began as British conservationists tried to rescue Brightness, a Beluga whale that escaped from a Ukrainian research lab into Turkish waters. Every story had its election angle . . .

'Hi! I'm Paddy Ashdown and I've got a message for Britain's floating voters . . .' *31 March*

Maharishi Mahesh Yogi's Natural Law Party was launched at a sell-out rock concert at the Royal Albert Hall featuring George Harrison and the Beach Boys. Supporters practised levitation or 'yogic flying'.

'Be honest, Millicent, have those Natural Law Party people been getting at you again?' *7 April*

The spectre of Arthur Scargill appeared on polling day, despite Labour's efforts to distance themselves from the unions. The NUM leader said pressure would be put on a Labour government to sack the British Coal chief.

'Not yet, boyos! Not yet!' *9 April*

There was widespread use of opinion polls and expert commentators by the media during the course of the election – most were wide of the mark in predicting the result. The Conservatives won by a comfortable majority.

'Well done, see you again in five years.' *10 April*

As Portugal's Antonio Pinto won the ADT London Marathon, Neil Kinnock announced his resignation. Front-runners in the race to replace him as Labour leader were John Smith and Bryan Gould.

'There's a Mr Smith canvassing opinions on who should lead Labour into the exciting election coming up in five years' time . . .' *13 April*

Roy Hattersley also resigned after Labour's election defeat and speculation mounted as to the pair's future careers. Meanwhile Euro Disney's Magic Kingdom opened in France.

'Okay, Neil and Roy, you're hired. But if you want to keep this job you're gonna to have to cheer up a bit . . .' *14 April*

Liverpool soccer manager, Graham Souness, toasted his team's FA Cup
semi-final success against Portsmouth from the Alexandra Hospital, Cheshire,
where he was recovering from triple heart-bypass surgery.

'I don't care how bored Mr Souness is, nurse. Get everybody back in bed!' *16 April*

The notorious Hole-in-the Wall ram-raiders gang struck for the fifth time over the holiday weekend, using a stolen JCB to scoop an Abbey National cash-machine containing £55,000 at Hempstead in Kent.

'I told you not to stop at the lights!' *21 April*

In the run-up to the Earth Summit on world resources Prince Charles, the future head of the Church of England, challenged the Vatican over the issue of birth control, saying that 'poverty and population grow together'.

'I told you we shouldn't fly over Highgrove!' *24 April*

The new Chief Justice, Lord Taylor, announced that he thought judges were getting out of touch with the public and could improve their image if they ceased to wear wigs and robes.

'I do hope for your sake, Montmorency, that the Chief Justice will resist the temptation to dispense with wigs and robes . . .' *30 April*

Pop-star Madonna launched her film-production company and caused a shudder in the Brontë Society when she revealed that she was considering playing the role of Cathy in a remake of *Wuthering Heights*.

'Madonna, honey – you shout: "Heathcliff, Heathcliff." Then run into his arms – GENTLY!' *1 May*

The Northern Examination and Assessment Board introduced a controversial new GCSE English Literature course whose syllabus included TV soap operas and comedy series such as *'Allo 'Allo* and *Monty Python*.

'Gentlemen, I'd like to introduce you to a new colleague, Professor Boggit, who achieved a distinction in *'Allo 'Allo* and *Neighbours* Studies . . .' *5 May*

The Queen's Speech at the State Opening of Parliament set out the new government's agenda, including a National Lottery by 1994 which would raise over £1 billion a year to fund the arts, sports, charities and tourism.

'. . . And now, in accordance with my Government's wishes – eyes down for a full house . . . clickety-click, sixty-six . . .' *7 May*

Following the much-publicized appointment of Stella Rimington as head of MI5, Sir Colin McColl was named as the head of MI6 in a move designed to lessen the obsessive secrecy surrounding Britain's intelligence services.

'Right, 007. These are your instructions. After you've passed them around the room – swallow them.'

8 May

The Archbishop of Canterbury, Dr John Carey, attacked the Tory vision of a free-enterprise Britain and recent massive pay-rises to top executives in a time of recession.

'Head down, sir. Archbishop Carey is angry.' *11 May*

Judith Ward was freed after serving 18 years for terrorist crimes she did not commit. Appeal judges said her repeated confessions to three IRA bombings were unreliable as a personality disorder had made her fantasize and tell lies.

'The poor woman certainly fitted the description of an IRA bomber – mentally unstable and living in a fantasy world.' *12 May*

Ireland's Catholic community were stunned when it was revealed that the Bishop of Galway, Dr Eamonn Casey, had syphoned off £65,000 of Church funds to support his former mistress and mother of his 17-year-old son.

'Usually he offers up the collection to the altar.' *14 May*

An 11-year-old schoolboy, David Stockhill, used his Lego set to invent an ingenious locking device to prevent car theft, which greatly impressed police and motor manufacturers.

'I don't care how ingenious this 11-year-old kid's anti-theft device is — I wanted an old-fashioned, shiny, comfy, stealable car!' *15 May*

After the separation of the Duke and Duchess of York, Fergie move to a £950,000 house in Surrey, taking daughters Beatrice and Eugenie with her.

'Hello, Fergie – it's Andrew. How did the move go? *18 May*

National Heritage Secretary, David Mellor, attacked overstaffing at the BBC which employs 25,000, and questioned the expenditure of licence-payers' money on building a £10 million village in Spain for the new soap *Eldorado*.

'Right, 'ere's the news – last night the Beeb responded to Dave Mellor's demand that they chuck out any overpaid geezers what's been wastin' all the readies . . .' *19 May*

In an attempt to improve their image after recent miscarriages of justice, Home Secretary Kenneth Clarke announced a top-level inquiry into the police, signalling one of the biggest shake-ups in their 150-year-history.

'Right, Hoskins – Kenneth Clarke's "Improve the Police Image", Section 4A – go in and ask the gentleman politely for his Bren Gun, then invite him round to the Station for tea and biscuits . . .' *21 May*

British Rail demonstrated a new device to secure 'death-trap' slam-doors on its Intercity trains after repeated criticism by watchdog organizations that too little was being done to protect the public.

'Well, at least BR have lashed out and made the doors safe.' *22 May*

Crowds flocked to coastal resorts as temperatures rose into the 70s on a rare, sunny Bank Holiday weekend. However, fears continued regarding the harmful effect of radiation due to the depletion of the ozone layer.

'Just how big do you reckon this hole in the ozone layer is, Norman?' *25 May*

As Britain experienced the worst drought for a century, the Prince of Wales' address to the Royal Society for Nature Conservation in Devon focused on the urgency to save water.

'Cook and I were wondering, Your Royal Highness, if we could have a quick rub down with some of the cooking sherry . . .?' *26 May*

Leaders from 115 nations gathered in Rio de Janeiro for the Earth Summit to save the planet and even up the balance between rich and poor countries. Britain's John Major led many of the key debates.

'It is a bird? Is it a plane . . .?' *1 June*

As water companies forecast record profits of £1.5 million during the drought, Scotland Yard announced a crackdown on crime, which had risen by 11% in the Metropolitan Police area.

'Come on out, we know you're in there!' *2 June*

Europe's blueprint for the future seemed in tatters as Denmark voted against the Maastricht Treaty. Many Tory Eurosceptics – including Margaret Thatcher – made their voices heard once more.

'**Actually, we Danes have a great respect for some of the British views on Maastricht . . .**' *4 June*

A new book on Princess Diana was published which suggested that she had attempted to take her life in despair at her unhappy marriage.

'Will that be everything, madam? All our Diana books and a box of matches . . .' *5 June*

Speculation on a rift between the Prince and Princess of Wales increased when a second book, Andrew Morton's *Diana: Her True Story*, appeared claiming to be based on information supplied by her close friends.

'Of course, if he'd been more romantic and stopped boredom setting in, none of this would have happened – pour us another cuppa, luv . . .' *9 June*

'Aye, it was on this very spot that Rudolf Hess parachuted down, booked his space of the beach, then went to talk to the authorities . . .' *12 June*

There was considerable excitement as Jeremy Bates beat Thierry Champion to become the first Briton to reach the fourth round of Wimbledon in 10 years. He subsequently fell to ninth seed Guy Forget.

'That reminds me – how did Jeremy Bates get on?' *30 June*

Many British holidaymakers were stranded as 12,000 French truckers blocked motorway routes and petrol stations across France in revolt against the introduction of new driving-offence penalties.

'Dear all. At last our misery is over. Three days stuck between huge French lorries carrying cognac, Nuit St Georges and garlic sausages.' *3 July*

The missing diaries of Nazi Joseph Goebbels were discovered and a storm broke as *Sunday Times* editor, Andrew Neil, appointed right-wing historian, David Irving, to transcribe them for serialization in the paper.

'Assistant fashion editor, eh? That's nice, Heinrich – Andrew Neil has given me a start as chief copytaker . . .' *6 July*

A national ballot of 18,000 dentists faced with a 7% cut in their NHS grants revealed that 80% were against registration of new NHS patients.

'Ah, c'mon, luv. You know we can't afford to go private.' *7 July*

Despite a 20-year campaign for the acceptance of women priests, 40% of lay members opposed the motion at a meeting of the General Synod of the Church of England – which requires a two-thirds majority for reforms.

'Y'know, Maisie – if they don't make up their minds soon about women priests, I'm going to have to consider something else . . .' *13 July*

A White Paper signalled the gradual break-up of the state monopoly of the railways, with private operators taking over selected routes under franchise. Many of the 2500 stations were expected to be sold off.

'Oh dear – how tiring, Gerald. Some persons here claim that nobody has told them their station's been sold.' *14 July*

President of the Board of Trade, Michael Heseltine, announced that the Post Office's loss-making parcel-delivery service, Parcelforce, would be privatized.

'I dunno, the service seems to have lost something since the privatization announcement . . .' *17 July*

A Press Complaints Commission ruled that media stories about the private lives of government ministers were in the public interest, after the *People* exposed Heritage Secretary John Mellor's affair with a 31-year-old actress.

'I'll have to go, love – got a busy day ahead. More dirt to dig on David Mellor and I've promised to take my wife out to lunch.' *21 July*

Merseyside Assistant Chief Constable Alison Halford accepted £142,600 and a pension of £35,836 a year in compensation for withdrawing allegations that sex discrimination had hindered her promotion in the police force.

'She says if she's not made Chief Constable immediately, she'll sue for sexual discrimination . . .' *23 July*

After 17 days of international pressure, Iraq relented and allowed UN weapons inspectors access to its Agriculture Ministry. Many commentators pointed out that any sensitive documents would by then have been destroyed.

'Well done, Mustapha – what did you do with the sensitive documents?' *28 July*

In an effort to move on hundreds of 'travellers', Social Security staff visited a camp in Wales to speed up payments required for fuel. Meanwhile a crackdown on moral standards in schools was announced by the government.

'I don't know why they can't leave that kind of thing to the parents . . .' *30 July*

There was a scandal at the Barcelona Olympics when three members of the British team were sent home after tests suggested that they had taken a banned drug.

'Remarkable! But if he can fill a specimen bottle from over there, he must be on drugs . . .' *31 July*

Singer Michael Jackson arrived in Britain for a national tour but had to pull out of a Wembley concert after contracting a virus. Jackson, who travels with a pet chimp, is known to have had extensive cosmetic surgery.

'Good news for the rest of the tour, Jacko baby – the doc had enough spare parts in his bag to build another one . . .' *3 August*

There was public outrage during the Balkan crisis when two children being evacuated by bus from an orphanage were killed in cross-fire along the notorious 'Snipers' Alley' outside the Bosnian capital of Sarajevo.

'Brilliant marksmanship, Stevo – considering they're such tiny targets.' *4 August*

Chancellor Norman Lamont broke his holiday to order a cut in interest rates in National Savings schemes as building societies suffered. Many believed that the move was too little, too late.

'We've just received a nice card from Mr Lamont, sir . . . "Having a super time . . . have cut National Savings interest rates a bit, hope that helps . . . lovely weather. Norman." ' *7 August*

As thousands fled the 'ethnic cleansing' practices of the rival factions in the strife-torn Balkans, refugee camps filled to capacity and there were calls for Britain and other EC nations to take more.

Ethnic Cleansing? *14 August*

After years of bad luck and frustration, 39-year-old Nigel Mansell drove to victory in the Formula One world motor-racing championships, the first Briton to hold the title since 1976.

'I take it Nigel Mansell made it, then?' *17 August*